The DESPERATE DAN BOOK

Printed and Published in Great Britain
by D. C. THOMSON & Co., Ltd., 185 Fleet Street,
London EC4A 2HS.
© D. C. THOMSON & Co., 1990
ISBN 0-85116-500-1

Later —

I'LL PAD MY HEAD WITH FOAM RUBBER AND BANDAGES.

FOAM RUBBER

NOT BAD, EH? NOW LET'S SEE HOW IT WORKS.

WAYHAY! AH CAN HEAD A BRICK — WITHOUT BREAKING IT!

AND IT WORKS EVEN BETTER WITH A BALL — JUST CALL ME DANNY LINEKER.

FIRST TIME I'VE EVER HEADED A BALL WITHOUT BURSTING IT!

DRAT IT! NOW I'VE BURST IT WITH A TOE-ENDER!

PHLLT!

PHSST!

So — I'LL PAD MY SIZE TWENTIES LIKE MY HEAD.

YOU'RE DARN TOOTIN'! I'M READY FOR THIS MATCH NOW.

But first the team photograph —

WHO'S THE ROVERS' NEW STRIKER, JOE?

LOOKS LIKE A SULTAN WITH SORE FEET TO ME!

The kick-off —

TO YOU, DAN.

WOW! WHAT A SHOT!

OOF!

9

FOR A FEW HOLLERS MORE...

ALL Dan wanted was a good "clean" fight, but Black Bart had other ideas . . .

15

B

FRISKY WHISKERS!

One whiskery week later —

26

QUAINT CHRISTMAS WEATHER, DANNY MAH BOY. AIN'T NEVER SEEN BLACK SNOW BEFORE.

Then at a side window —

HEY, UNCLE DAN! LOOKS LIKE A FIRE'S STARTED AT THE RAILWAY STATION.

SUFFERIN' SIDEWINDERS! NOW THE CURTAIN'S CAUGHT IN MAH BEARD!

MY NEW CURTAINS! WHAT **IS** GOING ON, DANIEL?

AW, SHUCKS! IT WAS JUST AN ITSY-BITSY ACCIDENT, AUNT AGGIE!

28

Then —

31

WELL AT LEAST AH'M NOT GETTIN' LOLLIPOPS THIS YEAR.

The day of grandpappy's departure —

HERE'S YOUR PRESENT, BIG BOY! BUT KEEP IT WRAPPED TILL YOU'VE TAKEN ME TO THE STATION. IT'LL BE MORE OF A SURPRISE.

TO DAN HAPPY XMAS

NO NEED TO TAKE A TAXI, GRANDPAPPY, I'LL RUN YOU TO THE STATION.

TAKE IT EASY, YOU BIG BABOON — YOU'RE RATTLIN' MY OLD BONES.

WONDER IF DAN HAS A LICENCE TO CARRY PASSENGERS?

C

Who can this be? Is it Dan's long lost sister?
Nope! It's dear old Desperate Dan himself.
But why in tarnation is he dressed so strangely?
Can Dan have gone soft?
Read on and see how Desperate Dan became . . .

The Desperate DAME

Looks like trouble in the audience.

I LOVE PANTOMIMES!

WHERE ELSE CAN I PINCH SO MANY GOODIES?

SWIPE!

WAAAH! A FAT MAN STOLE MY SWEETIES!

Oh, no! Double trouble . . .

HEY, KID! MOVE THAT PESKY BALLOON!

SHAN'T!

HAR! THAT SHOWED YOU, BRAT!

BANG!

SSSSHHH!

SSSHH!

DIDN'T YOU KNOW? EVERY PANTO NEEDS...

CUSTARD PIES

...A PIE FIGHT!

SPLURGE!

OH YEAH? HOW ABOUT...

...A COW-PIE FIGHT? HA-HA!

WHOOSH!

COW PIE

CRUMP!

OOF!

COSTUMES

SPLIT!

TEAR!

NEXT YEAR, WHY DON'T YOU DO 'CINDERELLA'?

43

The first heats were held in Shadow Creek.

MY MONEY'S ON MINNIE SQUAW-SQUAW . . . SWEETHEART OF THE SIOUX NATION!

WHEN I'M CALLING YOU—OO-OO-OO

YOU AIN'T NOTHIN' BUT A HOUND DOG!

SHEET MUSIC

When Dan's turn came —

COULD WE MOVE THIS STAGE A MITE . . . MY STAR COULD CATCH A COLD IN THIS WIND?

45

46

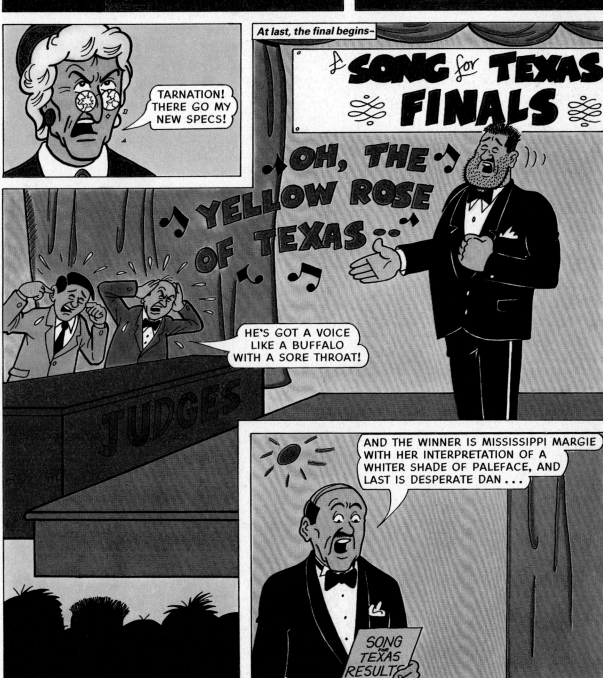

D

A CRACKER CHRISTMAS
A HUNDRED BUCKS FOR SIX CRUMMY CRACKERS! YOU'VE GOT TO BE KIDDIN' — PULL THE OTHER ONE!
Get your CHRISTMA CRACKERS HERE!
CHRISTMAS CRACKERS
CHRISTMAS CRACKERS

TIE UP THE ENDS WITH FENCE WIRE . . .

. . . AND TO THE GUY WHO CAN PULL IT — A WHOLE STILTON CHEESE! PHEW! IT'S STRONGER THAN ME!

So, at the Mayor's Christmas party.

A MERRY XMAS TO ALL

DAN'S CRACKERS

HERE'S MY CHRISTMAS PRESENT FOR YOU, MR MAYOR.

I DO DECLARE! THANK YOU KINDLY, DAN.

DO ME THE HONOUR OF PULLING THE FIRST CRACKER WITH ME, DAN.

IT'S A PLEASURE.

59

60

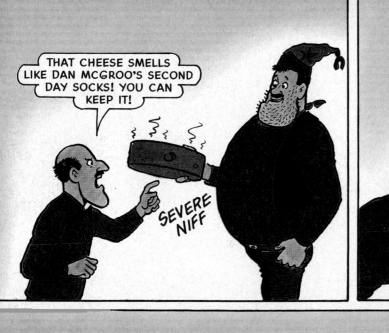

70

HOLIDAY BREAK!

IT'S GREAT TO SNIFF THEM SEA BREEZES! I'M GOING TO ENJOY MY SEASIDE HOLIDAY.

ONE PUNCH WINS A BAR OF TOFFEE!

ONCE AROUND THE DIAL WINS

TEST YOUR PUNCH

ONE PUNCH WINS ALL THE BARS OF TOFFEE!

BOP!

DOWN BALL

WHIRRR

CANDY

CANDY

CANDY

CANDY

TEST YOUR PUNCH

YOU SURE GET YOUR MONEY'S WORTH IN THIS TOWN!

GUESS YOUR WEIGHT

IF I'M HALF A STONE OUT, YOU GET DOUBLE YOUR MONEY BACK... I'D SAY YOU'RE ABOUT 16 STONE, SIR!

BOING!

CRACK!

CRUNCH!

JEEPERS!

I'VE SURE GOT MY MONEY'S WORTH AGAIN!

GRAND PIE-EATING CONTEST! FIRST PRIZE 50 DOLLARS

IT'S DAN! FILL UP SOME PIES WITH BRICKS, BOLTS, METAL — ANYTHING AT ALL!

I COULD WIN SOME BREAD HERE!

SURE ARE TASTY PIES!

GRUMBLIN' GRANNIES — DAN DOESN'T EVEN NOTICE THE FILLING!

KINDA CHEWY, THIS LAST PIE!

CRUNCH!

I'VE FINISHED MINE, SO I GUESS I'LL JUST HELP OUT THE REST OF YOU GUYS. YOU'RE KINDA STRUGGLING!

BAH! DAN'S GONNA SCOOP THE PRIZE!

DAN'S FAN

HERE COMES PREHISTORIC DAN, CACTUSVILLE'S VERY FIRST CAVE MAN! THAT NASTY MONSTER'S CAUGHT HIS EYE, AND IT'LL END UP AS DINOSAUR PIE!

PRIVATE DAN FOUGHT IN WORLD WAR ONE, HE'S THE ONLY SOLDIER WITHOUT A GUN. THOSE ENEMY SHELLS AIN'T A MENACE, HE USES THEM AS BALLS IN A GAME OF TENNIS!

'APPLEY' EVER AFTER!

THOSE ARE JUICY LOOKIN' APPLES YOU GOT ON YOUR TREE, UNCLE DAN!

PESKY VARMINTS! YOU JUST KEEP YOUR MITTS OFF THEM! GET OFF TO SCHOOL WITH YOU!

WHILE DANNY AND KATEY ARE IN SCHOOL, I'LL GO GET SOMETHING TO STOP 'EM PINCHING MY APPLES!

JOKE SHOP

TRICKS- NOVELTIES

STINK BOMBS

AND THIS IS THE PLACE TO GO!

GUFFAW! BET THAT'LL STOP 'EM ROBBIN' MY TREE!

HAT TRICKS!
JUST BLEW IN FROM CACTUSVILLE TO SEE HOW YOU'RE GETTIN' ALONG, GRANDPAPPY.
WHY, BLESS MY SOCKS, YOU YOUNG WHIPPERSNAPPER — GOOD TO SEE YOU. STEP INSIDE, DARN IT.

83

WELL, BURN MAH BRITCHES! WOULD YOU LOOK AT THAT?

THE TRUCK WHEELS HAVE SENT THAT HAT SKIDDIN' FARTHER THAN THE FIRST ONE.

NEXT GUY TO THROW!

THAT FLEABAG'S GRABBED MAH HAT!

GO ON, BOY. CARRY IT PAST THE OTHERS.

Alas—

HOI! QUIT CHEWIN' IT, YOU MANGY MUTT!

CHEW

The next competitor is purty smart . . .

SAY, KIDS, WHEN I THROW MY HAT, GET THEM LONGHORNS MOVIN' — AN' THIS FIVE DOLLAR BILL IS YOURS.

YAHOO!

YIP-YIP!

WELL BLOW ME! THEM KIDS MOVED THE CATTLE — JUST AS AH THREW!

DON'T GO TOO CLOSE, MISTER. RECKON IT'S FROM OUTER SPACE!

NO IT AIN'T! IT'S MY HAT! AND ITS SPEED OF LIGHT SET IT ALIGHT!

YOU AIN'T GETTIN' AWAY WITH THAT! YOU CAN'T PROVE THAT HEAP OF ASHES IS YOUR HAT! SO THAT WAS A FOUL THROW.

CALL ME A CHEAT, EH? WELL THAT'S SOMETHING I AIN'T!

WE'LL HAVE ONE MORE THROW, YOU OLD GOAT — GET THE GUYS TOGETHER!

DON'T GET YOUR BRISTLES IN A TWIST.

HAW-HAW! WHAT A SUCKER! YOU'LL HAVE TO BUY ALL THEM GUYS NEW HATS.

IVOR TITFER

HAT & WIG MAKER

THE LATEST HEADGEAR